# WOULD
# YOU
## RATHER?

JOE SHOOMAN

# WOULD YOU RATHER?

### THE ULTIMATE COLLECTION OF PREPOSTEROUS POSERS TO PONDER

JOHN BLAKE

First published in the UK by John Blake Publishing
An imprint of Bonnier Books UK
80–81 Wimpole Street, London, W1G 9RE
Owned by Bonnier Books
Sveavägen 56, Stockholm, Sweden

www.facebook.com/johnblakebooks 
twitter.com/jblakebooks 

First published in hardback in 2020

ISBN: 978-1-78946-388-0
eBook ISBN: 978-1-78946-440-5

British Library Cataloguing-in-Publication Data:

A catalogue record for this book is available from the British Library.

Design by www.envydesign.co.uk
Internal illustrations by Rachel Walsh

Printed and bound in Great Britain by Clays Ltd, Elcograf S.p.A.

3 5 7 9 10 8 6 4 2

Every reasonable effort has been made to trace copyright-holders of material
reproduced in this book, but if any have been inadvertently overlooked the
publishers would be glad to hear from them.

John Blake Publishing is an imprint of Bonnier Books UK
www.bonnierbooks.co.uk

'Life is the sum of all your choices'
ALBERT CAMUS

'Life is the name of the game
And I want to play the game with you'
BRUCE FORSYTH

# INTRODUCTION

**ALBERT AND BRUCE,** those two famous existentialist thinkers, have both already been proven right, because you are reading this. You chose to visit the website/bookstore/library. You chose to put this book in your basket. You chose to open it. You chose to continue reading to . . . hey, come back! This bit isn't very long and the good stuff starts in a minute.

Every day we face dilemmas: pyjamas or nude? Toast or cereal? Bath or shower? (And then we get thrown off the bus. Philistines.) At any stage we could all choose differently. Maybe wearing pyjamas would fend off a cold. Maybe the toast would burn and we'd go hungry and miss the bus. Maybe you decide to phone that person you fancy. And maybe they answer. Maybe you go on a date. Maybe you ask them to marry you. Maybe they say yes. Maybe you have children. Maybe all those children love reading. Maybe they all demand this book as a present. Maybe . . .

. . . Oh alright, it was a joke, sheesh. Seriously, it's warmer over here. Welcome back.

*Would You Rather?* brings together a collection of these everyday conundrums. It is at heart a book about the human experience. What dinosaur you choose may show the world what kind of person you are. Which technological advance you'd choose to make reveals something about your personality. And, which books you pick up certainly goes a long way to being the very sexiest, loveliest, brainiest, splendidest person that has ever lived. There's no two ways about that. (Oh, you stick around when there's compliments to be had, we see. Shameless.)

Enjoy this book. Some of the choices will need some deep thinking. Some will be a matter of gut reaction. Some are silly. You can be as honest with yourself as you like. There's no extra points for 'correct' answers, because there really ain't any rights or wrongs here. As life lessons go, that's not a bad one either.

# INTRODUCTION

Go well, folks, for we are all specks of dust in the eternal cosmos. Choices are there to be made. If you need any further inspiration, here's a quote from another world-famous philosopher:

> I don't want to see a ghost
> It's a sight that I fear most
> I'd rather have a piece of toast
> And watch the evening news
> DES'REE

# CONTENTS

*Would you rather have a set of questions about . . .*

TV and Movies? *Turn to page* 161

Triple Trouble? *Turn to page* 175


Or perhaps you'd rather read...


The Rules *Turn to page* xiii

About the Author? *Turn to page* 189

The Back Cover? *Turn to the Back Cover, obviously.*

Something Else? *Turn to page* 1 *in a different book.*

# THE RULES

*Would You Rather?* is a compendium of everyday dilemmas ... and some not-so-everyday ones too. You can open this book at any time, anywhere, and find a question to ask of yourself or others, pondering your choices at your leisure. The beauty of *WYR*, unlike life, is that there are no wrong answers – only funny, interesting, convincing and imaginative ones.

So shut your eyes, flick through these pages, let your finger land where it may – and a whole new world of fun awaits. Because contained in the question 'Would you rather...?' is also the unsaid follow-up query: *Why?* That, folks, is where things can get very silly, very informative and, we hope, very fun. There is nothing pointless about debate – philosophers have been making a living out of this kind of business for thousands of years. (Not a great living, admittedly. You don't see Ludwig Wittgenstein razzing around in a Porsche, as swathes of pneumatic supermodels feed him champagne-soaked tropical fruits.)

You can also play *Would You Rather?* as a turn-based game – here are some of our suggestions for how that might work. If you'd rather make up your own rules then that is also awesome...

# HOW TO PLAY

All you need is a pen or pencil and paper for each person, plus this book.

In order to decide who goes first you might want to:

♦ See who can jump/sing/ the highest.

  Roll a dice; the highest (or lowest) number goes first. Obviously decide beforehand whether it's low or high that wins.

♦ Have a race around the room.

♦ Offer something in return – i.e. doing the washing up or another chore.

# THE RULES

♦ Draw a playing card out of the pack each with the highest/lowest going first.

♦ Tell a joke to each other, taking turns, and the first one that laughs is out and does not go first. Repeat until one player remains.

♦ Thumb war.

♦ Arm-wrestling.

♦ Breakdance contest.

♦ All potential players go and join a Buddhist retreat, and spend years meditating on the nature of self and the life force. When all have attained nirvana and let go of ego and all earthly wants, who goes first in the game – like all human endeavour on a cosmic level – is entirely pointless. The game, perhaps, is life itself. And one's consciousness can choose to participate, or to merely observe all things.

## TWO-PLAYER GAME

Player 1 holds the book and reads a question: Would I rather...

Player 2 and Player 1 both write down the selected answer, i.e. what Player 1 would rather do. If they match, Player 2 gets a point. If they do not, Player 1 gets a point.

Repeat with Player 2 holding the book and reading a question: Would I rather...

Continue for ten rounds – the player with the most points is the winner. If scores are equal, sudden-death rules apply with the first to get a 'wrong answer' (one that is different from the questioner's) declared the loser.

# THREE-PLAYER GAME 1

As two-player game, except all three answers must be the same. A lot harder, depending on how well you know the questioner.

# THREE-PLAYER GAME 2

One player is designated the questioner as above, and the remaining two players decide what the questioner would rather do.

If: All three players' answers are the same, all receive a point.

If: The two players' answers are the same as each other's, but different from the questioner's, the questioner receives a point.

If: The two players' answers are different from each other, but one is the same as the questioner's, the questioner and the player with the correct answer each receive a point.

# THREE-PLAYER GAME 3

As three-player game 2, except two players are chosen to play – use some of the suggestions above to decide which two are in the hot seat, and who is the questioner. The questioner does not score points; their answers are the benchmark for the players. Anyone whose answer is the same as the questioner's gets a point. The questioner changes each round, to the left, so all get a turn. The game continues until there's a winner.

# MULTIPLE-PLAYER GAME 1

Everyone plays, as per three-player game 1. Tricky!

## MULTIPLE-PLAYER GAME 2

Two players go head-to-head. The questioner asks Would You Rather...? about every other individual in the room. So, if there are five people for example: Alice is questioner, and Hattie and Paul are the two players, Alice would ask something about the others in the room: e.g., first Jolene, then Archie.

## MULTIPLE-PLAYER GAME 3

As per three-player game 3.

*But I don't want to play by your rules. I'm a leader, not a follower.*

Yes, you are just allowed to have Dad/Mum/one person at the head of the table reading them out, and then arguing loudly about them as a family/ group until it inevitably descends into unruly shouted disagreement and Uncle Keith begins throwing sprouts at Aunt Gladys until she's started hallucinating/photosynthesising.

## VARIATIONS

Forfeits can be decided before the game, such as:

♦ Eat a whole sprout.

♦ Balance a sprout on your nose.

♦ Do five keepy-ups with a sprout (with whichever part of body you choose but not your hands).

♦ Buy some sprouts to replace all the ones that you've ruined.

♦ Solve Fermat's Last Theorem.

♦ Do the dishes.

♦ Recite the alphabet backwards.

♦ (Adults only) Take a drink.

♦ Talk in a silly voice for the next hour.

♦ Wear your clothes backwards for the rest of the day.

♦ Listen to your least favourite and most annoying song five times in a row on headphones without complaining.

♦ Stay silent for an hour.

Let your imaginations guide you and remember – have fun! We'd all rather have fun, after all.

# ANIMALS

Dr Doolittle is not only the name of
the laziest physician on the planet, but
also someone who could famously also
hold conversations with all manner of
creatures. But he differs from the man
with the plastic bags that stands near
the bins shouting at cats – animals
really do chat back to Dr D. If you
had the choice, would you like to talk
to the terrier next door – or would
you rather be their eternal king? The
world of animals, it seems, is full of
dilemmas...

Would you rather have a sausage dog in a hat or a puss in boots?

◆

Would you rather be able to talk with your pets or read people's minds?

◆

Would you rather be able to talk to animals or have them obey your every command?

Would you rather have a fully-grown elephant or a skunk as your constant companion?

◆

Would you rather have a pet cat the size of an elephant, or a pet elephant the size of a cat?

◆

Would you rather be a happy dung beetle or an unhappy butterfly?

Would you rather be a lion or a chimpanzee?

◆

Would you rather clean an angry baboon's teeth or a happy hippopotamus's bum?

◆

Would you rather be friends with a dolphin or be the only person who can see unicorns?

Would you rather have to date
Bigfoot or be stalked by an alien?

◆

Would you rather have the power
of echolocation but with poor
eyesight like a bat, or have the
power to navigate by vibrations but
only hear very low frequencies like
a snake?

◆

Would you rather teach a flea to
floss or teach a dog to dab?

Would you rather be a sloth, experiencing time veeerrryyyy slooooowly, or be a mayfly that rushes around doing everything in a single day – from birth to mating, marriage, fun and finally kicking the bucket?

Would you rather be licked on the face by a giraffe, or tickled by an octopus?

Would you rather be a honey bee or a honey badger?

Would you rather be a mountain
lion or an urban fox?

◆

Would you rather bring back the
thylacine (i.e. the Tasmanian tiger)
or the woolly mammoth?

◆

Would you rather be raised by
wolves like Romulus and Remus
(the founders of Rome) or raised by
apes like Tarzan?

Would you rather build an ark and sail the seas with every animal on board – which you'd have to clean up after – or be the manager of the biggest nature reserve in the world but have to deal with poachers?

◆

Would you rather spend a day as your favourite dinosaur, in modern times, or spend a month as yourself in dinosaur times?

Would you rather be an agile
mountain goat that can climb up
cliffs, or be an ostrich that can bury
its head in the sand and is also very
fast when riled?

◆

Would you rather have a hump like
a camel, so you could go fifteen
days without water, or have a
tongue like a woodpecker, that you
could wrap around your head?

Would you rather hide in a cave on land (with plenty of warm clothes) from a polar bear, or hide in an underwater cave (with breathing apparatus, of course) from a leopard seal?

◆

Would you rather be a vet or a pet?

◆

Would you rather have a job identifying every animal in the world by its poo, or have no sense of smell?

Would you rather be a worker ant
or a worker bee?

◆

Would you rather have camouflage
or have very, very sharp teeth and
talons or claws?

◆

Would you rather migrate to warm
countries every winter like a bird, so
you are constantly on holiday with
loads of others, or swim thousands
of miles like a blue whale, and be left
in peace and quiet?

# BOOKS

It is said that the world's first book was invented by Dave Books in the year 51. Regardless of the genesis of the folio, there have been over seven different books printed to date on such varied subjects as 'DIY PIE', 'Terrible Words for Pie' and 'PIE TIME'. There was also a thesaurus, but it wasn't very good, or even quite good or merely good. Here's some booky choices to wrestle with...

Would you rather have someone
ruin the end of every book you
read, or never be able to read in
peace and quiet?

◆

Would you rather have lunch with
your favourite character or with
your favourite author?

◆

Would you rather write an
unheralded literary classic or a
best-selling holiday romance
novel?

Would you rather read only
*War and Peace* or nothing at all
for a year?

◆

Would you rather read *War and
Peace* or eat it?

◆

Would you rather talk James Joyce
out of writing *Ulysses* or have the
power to recognise people that
claim to have read *Ulysses*, but
actually haven't?

Would you rather have a book
of magic spells that hummed
worryingly at night so you had
to keep it shut, or have a book
describing everyone who ever lived
but you could hear it murmuring
about you and laughing when you
were about to drop off to sleep?

Would you rather write a book
without using the letter 'e', or read
one like that?

Would you rather write a novel or a dictionary of made-up words?

Would you rather be an illustrator or a writer?

Would you rather write the world's longest ever book, or the world's shortest ever poem (or vice versa)?

Would you rather visit the ancient library of Alexandria whenever you like, or have the ability to wirelessly upload ebooks to your brain?

Would you rather know every rhyme for 'orange' and 'purple' or always get the highest-scoring word in a game of Scrabble?

Would you rather work in a library or in a bookshop?

Would you rather an invention of
yours become a household word,
like Hoover (vacuum) or decide
which new words go in a dictionary
one year?

Would you rather star in a graphic
novel or be a minor character in an
obscure but brilliant Manga?

◆

Would you rather learn the art
of bookbinding or the art of
calligraphy?

Would you rather be a monk
copying out arcane and wonderful
new knowledge that will change
the world day after day, or travel
the kingdoms of the medieval
world distributing those books and
having adventures?

◆

Would you rather invent
underwater paper or pens that
write with lava?

Would you rather be able to jump inside a book and mess about with the story, but if someone closed the book you were stuck until they opened it again and you fell out on top of them, or have the power to put someone else in a book, with the same conditions attached?

Would you rather have a haircut like Shakespeare, and be a minor character in one of his plays, or have a haircut like Joe Wicks and be an ingredient in one of his diet recipes?

Would you rather be a character in the *Canterbury Tales*, but one of the crude ones, or be a character in a Thomas Hardy novel, and be miserable all the time?

Would you rather know the first sentence of every book in the world, or the last sentence in every book in the world?

Would you rather judge a book by its cover or by its author?

Would you rather be in the
*Discworld* universe or in the world
of *Lord of the Rings*?

◆

Would you rather have the ability
to read a newspaper in any language,
or the ability to read people's faces
like a book?

◆

Would you rather travel with Jack
Kerouac or go fishing with Ernest
Hemingway?

Would you rather use a Kindle forever or accept that every book you read was the size of a church bible?

◆

Would you rather have floor-to-ceiling shelves of books, or be able to walk on the ceiling and read quietly without getting interrupted once a year?

Would you rather live in a funky and futuristic, exciting and dangerous dystopian novel, or live in a story of calm and wonderful unchanging peace where nothing was difficult and it was always just the right temperature for a nap?

◆

Would you rather a programmable computer voice narrated your audiobooks, or have Stephen Fry/ Joanna Lumley always do them?

# FOOD AND DRINK

One of humans' more endearing
pastimes is putting cold things in
special hot cupboards, and then
ingesting the results. It's also true that
humans are about 65 percent water,
most which is lost as tears when it
comes to paying bills. We're all on
the cook/eat/excrete/repeat diet, after
all. Still, there are as many different
choices of food and drink as there are
tastebuds on a tongue. Here's a few
WYRs to chew on.

Would you rather eat fifty sprouts
or one whole cabbage?

◆

Would you rather eat an ice-cream
that might have had a slug in it, or
eat a slug that tastes of ice-cream?

◆

Would you rather have pineapple
on your pizza or chocolate on
your chips?

Would you rather eat only
vegetables for a year or eat only
meat for a month?

◆

Would you rather have an
everlasting ice-cream, or an
everlasting bar of chocolate?

◆

Would you rather eat pudding
before dinner, or a starter after
dinner?

Would you rather appear
as a contestant in a cooking
competition, or be the host of one?

Would you rather eat a delicious
meal which you later find out
is made of insects, or know the
ingredients beforehand?

Would you rather feed the world's
hottest chili to your nemesis, or
eat the world's most delicious
strawberry?

Would you rather be a gourmet
or a wine tasting expert?

◆

Would you rather only be able
to taste sweet things or savoury
things?

◆

Would you rather have ice-cream
but only in the freezing cold
winter, or have your favourite
curry but only in the heat of the
summer?

Would you rather have meat substitute vegan sausages that taste somewhat like meat, or vegan sausages that taste of their own ingredients (like a Glamorgan sausage)?

◆

Would you rather have the crispy bits of a shepherd's pie from round the edge of the pan, or the succulent bit in the middle?

◆

Would you rather eat a whole lime or a whole bitter melon?

Would you rather have a lasagna
fresh from the oven, or heated up
the next day after all the flavours
have had time to make friends
and snog?

Would you rather run a late-night
kebab shop where most of the
clientele were drunk, or have a fleet
of food trucks, but they'd keep
breaking down in the middle of
busy roads?

Would you rather eat liquorice with Billie Eilish, or eat jello with Camila Cabello?

◆

Would you rather go to *La Tomantina* festival in Spain, where people have a huge tomato fight every August, or go to watch the World Hot Dog eating contest in the United States?

Would you rather be a master chef or a world-class baker?

Would you rather eat lab-grown meat or veggie faux-meat?

◆

Would you rather split the bill amongst everyone equally, no matter what they had, or be the one who calculates to the penny how much everyone owes?

◆

Would you rather dress up for a disappointing dinner out, or be scruffy for a disappointing dinner at home?

Would you rather drink a cup of tea which has got loads and loads of crumbs in it from dunking your own biscuit, or share a cup of tea with someone else from a cup which has no crumbs in it?

◆

Would you rather only eat things that you grew yourself, or have to always kill your dinner?

◆

Would you rather shuck and eat fresh oysters from their shells or cook a lobster alive?

Would you rather eat fugu (dangerous Japanese sushi fish) or eat a hundred worms alive?

◆

Would you rather spend a month eating a different cuisine each day, including ones that you don't like, or spend a year eating your favourite meal every day?

◆

Would you rather have a magic food-materialising machine which was stuck on Christmas dinner only, or never have Christmas dinner again?

Would you rather have to sing opera with a mouthful of beans live on television, or run through your street naked where only your neighbours could see you?

◆

Would you rather go to a Japanese food market where you didn't know what anything was on the menu, but had to point at it and hope, or go to Japan and only eat at McDonald's and other fast food chains all the time?

Would you rather eat one dingo-butt burger live on television or have gruel every night for a month?

◆

Would you rather have the taste buds of a catfish (almost twenty times as many as a human), or a tongue the same length as an anteater's so you could reach the very last morsels at the bottom of any jar or bottle? (You might also want to ask your partner what their answer would be on this one.)

# FORFEITS/ BIZARRE

Imagination. It's good, isn't it. Imagine not having an imagination. You literally can't. What we can do is imagine some weird and wonderful stuff, like a dog that can breathe fire and talk about politics from the other end. See? That's an image in your head now. You're welcome. And in an infinite multiverse, that dog actually exists. Here's some more examples from the left-field of our increasingly redundant brains.

Would you rather have to eat an insect every day, or eat roadkill once?

♦

Would you rather look ten years older from the neck up, or from the neck down?

♦

Would you rather have everyone always be able to read what you're thinking, or always be able to see what you're doing?

Would you rather try to survive on a desert island for one week, or on a snow-covered mountain peak for one night?

Would you rather be able to morph into a fire engine's siren, or change into an ice-cream van's chimes?

Would you rather swim alone with sharks, or have to grab a rhino's tail?

Would you rather have to run from an axe-wielding murderer or fight a big, angry dog?

◆

Would you rather run naked through a shopping centre, or walk around all day with a sign that says, 'I am a silly, silly sausage who drinks wee wee'?

◆

Would you rather run five hundred miles, and then run five hundred more – to fall down at your crush's door – or join a dating site?

Would you rather have to hold
in your farts for an hour, or fart
whenever you wanted to but accept
that everyone else was allowed to do
the same?

Would you rather fight one rabbit-
sized wasp, or a thousand wasp-sized
rabbits?

♦

Would you rather roll a stone up a
mountain with your nose or count
every grain of sand in a sandbox?

Would you rather spend a year building up only one part of your body, or get up at 4am every day for a year to run around the block?

◆

Would you rather talk backwards all day, or walk/chair backwards all day (at school, or work, or in your role as Pope)?

◆

Would you rather be able to identify individual snowflakes or to count individual raindrops?

Would you rather be able to turn your foot into a shovel, but it stays like that all week, or spin your head all the way around, but it makes you sick later when you are alone?

◆

Would you rather buy an all-day bus pass and travel backwards and forwards to the same place to get your money's worth, or pay triple the normal price so you don't have to?

Would you rather wrestle a giant octopus or play tennis with a giant spider?

◆

Would you rather be best mates with Godzilla, but it meant you had to crush whole cities periodically, or have Godzilla round for dinner and save the city, but it meant you had to somehow find ten tons of fish and chips to feed him?

Would you rather spend a week
encased in a box of ice, where
nobody could see more than a
silhouette of you, or spend a week
suspended in a perspex box above
London where people could see
everything you did?

◆

Would you rather be the inspector
of moustaches, with specific
rules on what is and what is not
acceptable, or be the outlaw
El Moustachio, who goes around
at night gluing enormous taches
onto household items?

Would you rather have to try and dig a tunnel to the Earth's core, or try to build a ladder to the Moon?

◆

Would you rather have a spaceship that had an everlasting battery, but could only go at 60 miles an hour, or have a hot air balloon that could turn invisible?

◆

Would you rather lose the ability to lie, or have to believe everything you hear?

Would you rather work as a living statue to replace statues that were being cleaned, and the pigeons would do what pigeons do on you instead, or work as an artist's nude model in a class where all your friends were enrolled?

◆

Would you rather be able to mimic the accent of anyone on TV, or have a torso that could morph into anyone's from TV?

Would you rather grow your arms to a hundred feet like Mr Tickle, but they stayed like that for a whole day, or shrink yourself to the size of a pea when you wanted, and risk being trodden on by your cat?

◆

Would you rather be able to shoot hard balls of snot from your nose that knock out your enemy, or produce stinks so bad that they incapacitate all around you?

Would you rather have a new
disease named after you or a new
species of cockroach named
after you?

◆

Would you rather have a personal
raincloud that followed you around
wherever you went, or have one
giant toe that always got sunburnt?

◆

Would you rather go to Antarctica
in a car with Ant, or sail to Quebec
with Dec around your neck?

# HISTORY

The funniest thing happened last night at 10.30 – and it was an absolute historical first. The skies parted, and a whole bunch of male humans dropped to the floor from special clouds. It was really quite awful and a few of them died; a high percentage are maimed for life. Can't help feeling that all those women saying 'hallelujah' were a bit misguided. History: there's lots of it. And here are some questions about it, which were written in the past (compared to when you're reading this bit).

Would you rather have lived in ancient Rome or Victorian London?

◆

Would you rather go back to see the dinosaurs, or head 1,000 years into the future?

◆

Would you rather have the first ever water-closet toilet, sink and power shower, or still use buckets which you could throw out of the window and maybe hit people you didn't like?

Would you rather have been there for the embroidering of the Bayeux Tapestry, or been there when the Lascaux Cave Paintings were done?

Would you rather have been present at the building of Stonehenge, or witnessed the building of the Pyramids?

Would you rather hear a Mammoth's moo, or see a T-Rex doing a poo?

Would you rather walk across the prehistoric land bridge from Asia to America, on the Baring Bridge, or be one of the first humans to walk from the Rift Valley toward Europe and Asia?

◆

Would you rather have plotted with Guy Fawkes and not been caught, or been the person that caught Guy Fawkes?

Would you rather have been a Roman Emperor or an Egyptian Pharaoh?

◆

Would you rather have been a pre-fame member of the Spice Girls, or be a future, non-original member of a girl band touring decades later in holiday camps and making a living out of it?

Would you rather be able to smell any historical period, and reconstruct the living conditions accurately from the aromas, or be able to touch any historical person that appeared in a painting, but who can smack you in the chops if you're being inappropriate?

◆

Would you rather be a Musketeer or a King?

Would you rather kiss Cleopatra or cuddle Tutankhamun?

◆

Would you rather have a drink with a Neanderthal, or play hopscotch with Homo Habilis?

◆

Would you rather be the first person to fly a plane, or the first to have gone deep underwater in a submersible?

Would you rather be a friend
of Nikola Tesla, or study with
Marie Curie?

◆

Would you rather go out for
dinner with Boudicca, or with
Julius Caesar?

◆

Would you rather go back to the
Ice Age and ride a mastodon, or go
forward in time and live on Mars?

Would you rather go back in time to the 1969 Woodstock Festival, or to the Sex Pistols' 1976 Manchester Lesser Free Trade Hall gig?

◆

Would you rather go back in time and talk with Jesus, or go back in time and talk with Buddha?

◆

Would you rather be able to witness the Big Bang, or the Big Crunch (the end of it all)?

Would you rather be part of Greek mythology, or part of the Norse sagas?

Would you rather go back in time and be a mod, or go back and be a rocker?

Would you rather go back in time and interview the very first person who thought to fry an egg, or the very first person who ever thought of eating chicken?

Would you rather go back in time and interview the first Homo Sapiens, or go forward in time and interview the very last person who ever lived?

Would you rather be a gumshoe private detective in the 1920s, or an undercover police officer in the 1960s?

Would you rather ride into battle with Joan of Arc, or battle for a ride on Noah's Ark?

Would you rather be a Geisha in ancient Japan, or be a lady of the court in Victorian England?

Would you rather have the power to transfer people from one time period to another, or have the power to visit different time periods without affecting anything?

Would you rather go for a holiday to an Iron Age hillfort, or go on holiday in a spaceship?

Would you rather research and write a book on the history of weeing off of waterfalls or write a book on the mechanics of pooing in space?

◆

Would you rather study philosophy in Ancient Greece, where you risk getting denounced like Socrates and forced to drink poison, or have a good old talk with a pharaoh in Ancient Egypt who might brick you up alive in a pyramid for being cheeky?

# MONEY

Money, money, money, money, money, money, money. Add a K and it's monkey. We know what we'd prefer to have, and it's the one that eats bananas. Nonetheless, the old folding stuff is an unfortunately vital aspect of commerce in the failing capitalist system we must all adhere to until we discover renewable and free energy, rendering ideas of scarcity and presumed value finally irrelevant. Fiat currency is the biggest delusion of humankind, and empires will fall. Right now, though, we'll have to debate a few bits'n'bobs of cash-related questions.

Would you rather work from home
or in a fancy office?

◆

Would you rather do something
you love for low pay, or something
you hate for high pay?

◆

Would you rather be paid
£1 million in one go, or £40,000
a year indefinitely?

Would you rather the UK operated
with a moneyless barter system,
or a fully planned and centralised
economy?

◆

Would you rather have
£1 million all in one pence pieces,
or £750,000 as a digital transfer?

◆

Would you rather win
£1 million and lose half of it, or
win £400,000 and keep it?

Would you rather that everyone was paid the same, or some randomly earned more than others (and you were one of the top earners)?

◆

Would you rather be able to print extremely good banknotes (but not completely undetectable – about 90 per cent of the time they'd fool everyone), but only one note per week, or find a pound coin on the floor every day?

Would you rather invest in the newest cryptocurrency fad, or bury £20,000 in your garden that you couldn't dig up for five years?

Would you rather play the same lottery numbers for every game, every week, or play random numbers when you felt like it?

Would you rather be paid by the day or by the year?

Would you rather trust your investments to a stockbroker who studied all the trends in the FTSE, or invest the same money yourself by throwing a dart, blindfolded, into the company listings of each day's newspaper?

◆

Would you rather have to sit inside an automatic ATM machine all day handing out money to people through the slots, or sit inside a speak-your-weight machine telling people how heavy they were?

Would you rather be a partner in a moderately successful investment bank, or be the financial advisor to a failing but lucrative banana republic?

◆

Would you rather be sponsored a pound a day to never say the word 'fiddlesticks' ever again (if you did you'd have to pay it all back), or pay ten pounds and be able to say 'fiddlesticks' whenever you liked?

Would you rather be a bookmaker
or a politician?

◆

Would you rather be known as a
great philanthropist, or the world's
first trillionaire?

◆

Would you rather have to give a
dog a five pound note each week,
or receive a ten pound note in the
dog's poo once a week?

Would you rather earn a million pounds, then burn it like KLF did, or earn a thousand pounds and keep it on condition that you incinerated your smartphone and didn't replace it for a month?

◆

Would you rather pay someone a small fortune to do your tax return, or do it yourself and potentially make mistakes that could cost you money and might get you put in jail?

Would you rather rob from
the rich and give to the poor,
or introduce a Universal Basic
Income?

◆

Would you rather be a professional
coin counter paid a very good wage,
or be a professional card counter
who could sometimes break the
bank, but risks getting found out
and banned from all casinos?

Would you rather live your life on credit and have to pay it back so you'd be skint sometimes, or never spend what you didn't have in the bank?

◆

Would you rather run a business selling dodgy, ineffective but very cheap cures for ailments, or run a business selling reliable medicines on condition that you owned all the patents so could send the prices sky-high?

Would you rather play poker against someone with diamonds for teeth, or arm-wrestle a chimpanzee and earn a hundred pounds, even if you lost?

◆

Would you rather put all your money on a 50/50 game of chance, or move to an island for a year where the only currency is what you produce, in a barter system?

Would you rather inherit
£1 million which was all yours to
keep, or be challenged to spend
£10 million in a month after
which, if you successfully got rid of
it all with nothing to show for it,
you'd inherit £100 million?

◆

Would you rather be the world
Monopoly champion who is
rubbish with personal finances,
or have a reasonable grasp of your
incomings and outgoings but often
lose at Monopoly, and get properly
enraged when you do?

Would you rather own a computer drive with some cryptocurrency on it, which you're not sure you have the correct password to and don't know how much it's worth, or sell it for ten thousand pounds?

◆

Would you rather have a £1 coin that magically reappeared in your pocket the week after you spent it, or have a £1 scratchcard that was guaranteed to make its money back 5 times out of 10, the other times either losing entirely or winning more than you paid for it?

Would you rather have a computer chip in your finger that was automatically recharged with cash every few months so you could just point it at things you wanted to buy, or get paid every week by cheques that you had to physically go to the post office to change into folding dosh?

◆

Would you rather lose all your money, or lose one of your senses?

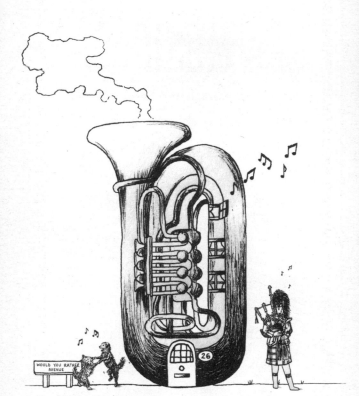

# MUSIC

God, it is widely known, gave rock and roll to you. Put it in the hearts of everyone. That said, the Devil has all the best tunes, which leads us to the logical conclusion that God is a Status Quo fan whilst the Devil would rather have a proper listening session to the entire Stax back catalogue. But enough exegesis, let's talk about pop pop pop music. Pop. Pop. Pop. Music.

Would you rather be a rock star or a film-score composer?

◆

Would you rather master the guitar or the piano?

◆

Would you rather be able to sing incredibly or play every instrument averagely?

Would you rather be a one-hit wonder or be in a struggling but highly praised cult band?

◆

Would you rather play a 10-foot guitar or a 10-inch guitar?

◆

Would you rather be able to hear every note of every instrument all the time during a song, or have the power to mute any instrument at will?

Would you rather join a boyband
and tour the world, or be in a band
that sells a decent amount, but
would never be as famous?

◆

Would you rather make music that
helped the yield of cows' milk, or
make music that was used by the
military to scare enemies?

◆

Would you rather be in *Stomp* or
be in *Glee*?

Would you rather wear shades inside all the time, or be infamous for being a rocker that never washed?

Would you rather be the world's best nose flute player, or write best-selling music that only dogs could hear?

Would you rather be an iconic pop-rap artist or a controversial one?

Would you rather be able to play guitar with your teeth like Jimi Hendrix or play piano with your feet like Jerry Lee Lewis?

◆

Would you rather date Katy Perry or manage Katy Perry?

◆

Would you rather invent a new instrument or master any instrument you choose?

Would you rather be the talentless pop star who sings (heavily autotuned) over other people's songs their whole career, or the talented but underpaid writer that creates those songs but gets a fraction of the money?

◆

Would you rather sing a saga of raga with Lady Gaga, or ride a big dipper made of a kipper with Dua Lipa?

Would you rather be able to scream like James Brown, or dance like Kate Bush?

♦

Would you rather play the world's smallest violin whenever someone was feeling sorry for themselves without a good reason, or play the world's biggest drum kit when someone was feeling a bit too big for their boots?

Would you rather slam dunk da funk, or put the bomp in the bomp de bomp de bomp?

Would you rather play the church organ incredibly loudly but not that well, or play the bagpipes pretty well but only know about six different tunes?

Would you rather play in Taylor Swift's backing band, or be the guide vocalist on her unreleased demos?

Would you rather be a busker on the guitar, or be a backing singer in an unsuccessful covers band?

◆

Would you rather be Elvis in the 1950s pre-army rock and roll dangerous days, or be Elvis in the 1968 comeback special and early Vegas days?

◆

Would you rather be able to play the piano, or be able to lift a piano up over your head?

Would you rather be known as the worst opera singer of all time, or be feted as one of the worst lead guitarists of all time?

◆

Would you rather have singing lessons from Freddie Mercury, or astrophysics lessons with Brian May?

◆

Would you rather play the Phantom of the Opera or play Queen Grizabella in *Cats*?

Would you rather live inside a house shaped like a tuba, so when the wind blew it would sometimes blast out very deep notes which would shudder you across the floor like a broken tumble dryer, or live in a house shaped like an acoustic guitar, where occasionally giants would pick it up and play it, losing their massive plectrums in the sound hole which could bonk you on the bonce if you weren't alert?

Would you rather play an edible instrument, or be able to make tunes from the sound of doing the washing up?

Would you rather look nothing like Ed Sheeran, but make a reasonable living out of playing the songs of his that you hated the most, or be his doppleganger and also have the same name, but have a punk band that you loved?

# SKILLS AND SUPERPOWERS

You can't move for superheroes these days can you? In the good old days, we just had Friedrich Nietzsche's Superman franchise to rely on, with old series of Burt Ward-era *Batman* occasionally appearing on BBC2. Now it's Marvel this, DC that, spin-offs like *Ironing Man* and *The Great Soprendo do Dallas* becoming the box office smash of the year. Pah! Who wouldn't want to have superpowers, though? The potential is endless, and so we've compiled some searching questions we acquired from a passing radioactive spider.

Would you rather be the world's fastest person, or the world's strongest?

◆

Would you rather be able to teleport anywhere instantly, or rewind time?

◆

Would you rather be able to speak ten languages fluently, or be a scientific genius?

Would you rather cure cancer
or solve the problem of climate
change?

◆

Would you rather have three legs
or three arms?

◆

Would you rather be able to fly or
be able to breathe underwater?

Would you rather have super vision
or super-sensitive hearing?

◆

Would you rather have a pause
button for life, or an instant erase
button for recent mishaps?

◆

Would you rather have a bottom
that could break the Internet, or
have a bottom that could turn to
steel, but only for five seconds
at a time?

Would you rather be able to shoot lasers from your eyes that could melt metal, or be able to regenerate into a new body if you got hurt?

◆

Would you rather be able to split yourself into six independent versions of yourself, but it'd give you a migraine the next day when they all snapped back, or temporarily expand your intellect so you could understand everything in the world, but then forget it all the next day?

Would you rather have absolute control of your body, or absolute control of your mind?

Would you rather have a photographic memory or be an empath?

Would you rather have springs in your feet so you could jump over houses, or a face that could change to the face of anybody you've met?

Would you rather be able to travel between different universes, but only to the same room you're currently in, or be able to stay in one place for ten days without moving, and nobody could bother you or make you do work or homework?

◆

Would you rather have the power of the wind, or the power to give your enemies windy bums at inappropriate moments?

Would you rather be able to turn water into your favourite drink, or turn your enemy's favourite drink into water?

◆

Would you rather be able to belch the alphabet backwards, or fart the national anthem?

◆

Would you rather be able to sleep with your eyes open, or speak with your mouth closed?

Would you rather have the power of teleportation (though you'd have to get the bus back), or be able to read minds – but only of sports referees?

◆

Would you rather be able to hypnotise eels, or be able to instantly know whether you did, in fact, leave the oven on when you left the house to go on holiday?

Would you rather have the ability
to make plants grow really fast, or
have the agility to climb up the
tallest redwood in the forest?

◆

Would you rather be able to
summon dolphins to swim with, or
summon eagles to fly with?

◆

Would you rather be able to slowly
walk down the hall faster than
a cannonball, or be able to write
lyrics that made sense?

Would you rather be blessed with
the knowledge that you are a genius
at DIY, but rarely use your skills,
or be the world's best maker of flat-
pack furniture, but never be able to
find the instructions?

◆

Would you rather be able to
remember every single sports result
that ever happened, or be able to
forget every time your team lost?

Would you rather be able to stay awake for a year (and then have to sleep for a year), or sleep every four hours, then be awake for four hours, and so on?

♦

Would you rather explore galaxies using your special power of remote viewing, or have an inbuilt ability to float in your sleep?

♦

Would you rather grapple with giants, or play pinball with pixies?

Would you rather be a powerful
warrior with a special sword and
magic armour, or be the steadying
influence on society that allows the
frictionless mixing of all people?

◆

Would you rather be able to make
an apple tree drop all its fruits by
staring hard at it for an hour, or
be able to kick a strawberry two
hundred feet in the air but only
when nobody was looking?

# SPORTS

Sports are vital social glues. Without golf, for example, presidents would be in their offices more often and who knows what disasters would ensue. The great game of hand-egg, which our US cousins erroneously call 'football', is a great way for giant steroid men dressed as astronauts to have lovely cuddles, thus ensuing mutual understanding and a karmic departure from toxic masculinity. Yes, Orwell called it 'war without the shooting' but he clearly never attended a grudge derby match between two drug dealer-backed teams in South America. Sport. Lots of it, isn't there?

Would you rather be a solo champion or part of a winning team?

◆

Would you rather be the greatest at a low-paying sport or mediocre at a high-paying sport?

◆

Would you rather play fifty games for your most hated rivals (and get paid), or play once for your favourite team?

Would you rather your team was sponsored by a dodgy company, and was therefore all but guaranteed to win trophies, or was sponsored by an ethically sound organisation that didn't have the resources to compete, so you had to really have a great season to win anything?

◆

Would you rather lose in a semi-final or in a replay of the final?

Would you rather score an own goal in a cup final, but your team still wins, or score the best ever hat-trick in a cup final, but lose?

◆

Would you rather stick with your hometown team, supporting them through thick and thin (and it's mostly thin), or without feeling any guilt at all switch your allegiance to a bigger club that wins things (and keep switching your support when they go rubbish)?

Would you rather be a high jump champion, or a long jump champion?

Would you rather play Kabaddi to international level or represent your school at table tennis?

Would you rather have boxed against Muhammad Ali or Mike Tyson in their prime?

Would you rather take five wickets in an innings, or score fifty runs in an innings?

Would you rather win first place in a gurning contest, or be a spectator to the same gurning contest, but you accidentally win third place?

Would you rather be run out on 99 runs, or take the wicket of someone who is on 99 runs?

Would you rather be a professional snooker player, or a professional pool trickshot demon?

◆

Would you rather play rugby union or rugby league?

◆

Would you rather be the referee at the World Cup final in your favourite sport, or play for your favourite team for ten years and never win anything?

Would you rather invent a brand-new move in snowboarding, or win the badminton world title?

♦

Would you rather play baseball or hockey?

♦

Would you rather be an esports champion, or run a hundred marathons in your life but always finish in the middle?

Would you rather be the best player ever at your favourite sport, but through a series of bad decisions and rank bad luck never fulfil your potential, or be an honest mid-paced plodder who just about carves out a career for themselves, without winning anything?

◆

Would you rather be the puck in an ice hockey match, or the ball in a tennis game?

Would you rather be a mountain of solid muscle, or have a lean hunter-tribesperson's body?

Would you rather compete in the World's Strongest Person championships, or compete in the Hunger Games?

Would you rather be a 100-metre champion, or a marathon champion?

Would you rather compete as a runner in desert ultramarathons, or compete in the 24 Hours of Daytona car race?

Would you rather be a Korfball superstar or an Ultimate Frisbee champion?

Would you rather be a horse racing commentator, or a cricket commentator?

Would you rather have a special
move named after you in judo, or
win a bronze medal in the
ski jump?

◆

Would you rather be part of
an Olympic team, or a part
of a World Championship /
World Cup Squad?

Would you rather hold the world record in your favourite sport but lose it after a week, or win several championships but never get near the world record?

◆

Would you rather have an extendable foot that would help you keep touching the floor when you reached for awkward snooker shots, or a head that could inflate when you were standing guarding the near post at footy corners?

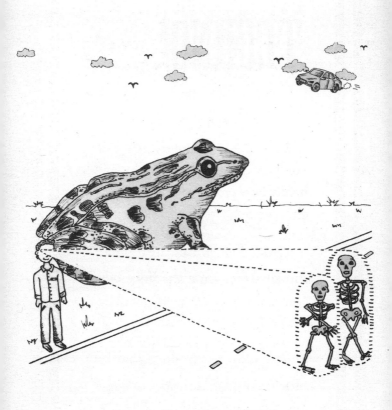

# TECHNOLOGY

When David Computer invented
computers in the year 1570, he could
hardly have predicted just how reliant
on technology we'd end up. Yes, folks,
we live in the Internet of Things,
apparently, and although we were
actually expecting jetpacks and flying
cars by now, we've got things like
fridges that tell you off just because the
salad I bought has rotted like it always
does, and now I'm in trouble with my
household appliances as well as with my
significant other. Bring on the robot
butlers, we say! But before that, how
about we ponder...

Would you rather use Apple or Microsoft – or to put it another way, Mac or PC?

◆

Would you rather have a mostly speedy Internet that goes painfully slow on occasion, including during games, video calls and uploads, or no Internet at all on the weekend?

◆

Would you rather have Netflix or Amazon Prime?

Would you rather have a lightsaber
or a laser gun?

◆

Would you rather have a car that
could fly, or a car that could turn
into a submarine?

◆

Would you rather have a 3D printer
that could sing, or a 3D printer that
could make replica objects with a 1 in
200 chance of decisively exploding
the first time you used them?

Would you rather own AI, but it's a hoover, or have a self-aware toaster?

◆

Would you rather upload yourself to the Internet permanently, or put your brain in a non-transferable robot body in the real world?

◆

Would you rather be a blob in a lava lamp, or the drum in a washing machine?

Would you rather have all your favourite music on vinyl records, or unlimited digital downloads?

◆

Would you rather profit hugely from creating an AI that then wages war on humans, or be the person that accidentally breaks the Internet forever for all humanity?

◆

Would you rather have mechanical teeth or a battery-powered belly?

Would you rather have a radio that could make people quote from *The Archers* when you pointed it at them, or a television that you could jump into and join in with the shows, but if someone turned the TV off you were stuck inside?

◆

Would you rather have a self-cleaning toilet that complimented you on the size of your plops, or trousers that could talk but which would swear at inopportune moments?

Would you rather live in the world of *Minecraft* or the world of *Animal Crossing*?

◆

Would you rather be a games programmer or a games tester?

◆

Would you rather have a genuinely AI robot pal, but which was actually really dense and stupid, or inject special molecules into your bloodstream that made you glow in the dark?

Would you rather have a drawer full of useful leads and plugs, but they were always blimmin' tangled and it took ages to find what you needed, or have wireless technology, but the batteries wore out super-regularly so you were forever replacing them?

◆

Would you rather be able to transform into a car, or turn into a gigantic frog every time you wanted to cross a road?

Would you rather work for Cyberdine Systems – but Skynet turns self-aware and starts making Terminators – or work as an IT assistant on a Klingon warship?

◆

Would you rather replace all your bones with very strong but slightly magnetic metal, or replace all your skin with a special hard-wearing plastic which was pretty slippery in the rain?

◆

Would you rather be a spammer or a hacker?

Would you rather have a robot Richard Osman living in your spare room, or two robot Alexander Armstrongs living in your shed?

♦

Would you rather invent a perpetual-motion device, or have one in your house that you didn't tell anyone about?

♦

Would you rather have X-Ray vision or laser vision that could cut steel?

Would you rather grapple with the ethics of personal robot assistants that looked, walked and talked like real humans but would do anything you said – 'Yes, anything, that's right. Wink wink' – or *be* a personal robot assistant that looked, walked and talked like real humans but had to do anything a human said – 'Yes, anything, that's right. Wink wink'?

◆

Would you rather play a game based on your real life, or play a character in a game based on someone else's real life?

Would you rather invent a time travel machine that could only go five minutes forward or backwards, or receive emails from someone who claimed they had invented one?

◆

Would you rather have a PiePad or a Crablet?

◆

Would you rather invent a pillow that could sing you to sleep, or invent a duvet that could give you a back rub?

Would you rather have an automatic bath that could walk to you wherever you were in the world, but sometimes would get lost and follow strangers home at 3 a.m., shouting your address at them so they'd phone you irately demanding you come and collect it, or have a shower that randomly didn't trust you to wash yourself properly so would shoot jets at varying hot and freezing temperatures at crevices you would rather it hadn't (even occasionally when you were actually asleep in bed)?

# TV AND MOVIES

It's the drug of the nation: it breeds ignorance and feeds radiation. That's television, if the Disposable Heroes of Hiphoprisy are to be believed (note: they usually are). Conversely, on Saturday night at the movies it's not that important which film you see, if the Drifters are to be believed (note: they're a bit sketchy, so it's up to you). One thing you can say about both the big and small screen is that they're screens of various sizes. Anyway, here's some tense set-ups to resolve at the end of the third act. . .

Would you rather have to watch
Bambi's mum die every day
forever, or eat Babe the pig?

◆

Would you rather have to watch
*Sharknado* once a week forever,
or never be able to watch any film
until it was two years old?

◆

Would you rather win an Oscar for
one serious film or be a comedy
film superstar?

Would you rather appear in
*EastEnders* or *Coronation Street*?

Would you rather be a heroic
Jedi do-gooder or an awesomely
powered Dark Side Sith?

Would you rather be in *The
Godfather* or in *Goodfellas*?

Would you rather live in the *Harry Potter* universe or in the *Pokémon* universe?

◆

Would you rather be Homer Simpson or Mr Burns?

◆

Would you rather be a newsreader or an on-the-ground reporter?

Would you rather write the worst ever episode of a smash-hit show, or the best-ever pilot episode of a show that never got commissioned?

◆

Would you rather watch the *Star Wars* movies in the order they were released (IV–V–VI, I–II–III, VII–VIII–IX) or consecutively from I to IX?

Would you rather be Supergirl with all her powers but with a weakness to Krypronite, or be the criminal mastermind always attempting weird and dangerous ways to alter reality and take over the world?

◆

Would you rather travel through time but only within the scenes of movies, or be able to change the plot of any movie that you are currently watching?

Would you rather be a reality TV show star for one year, or present the same reality TV show for five years?

◆

Would you rather clean the toilet of The Mountain or hand-wash the underpants of all the rest of the cast of *Game of Thrones*?

◆

Would you rather be the cool baddie in a Spaghetti Western, or be the good guy who doesn't get the girl in a romantic comedy?

Would you rather date a character in *Friends* in real life, or replace a character in *Friends* with a very cute dog?

◆

Would you rather be Marilyn Monroe or a friend of Marilyn Monroe?

◆

Would you rather receive a hundred Oscar nominations but never win, or receive one nomination and win but posthumously?

Would you rather be a background actor in the best movie of all time, or the lead actor in the worst?

◆

Would you rather travel the world scouting locations for TV and movies, but rarely be at home and receive little credit, or make hit movies but live in a huge gated mansion that is isolated from the rest of the world?

Would you rather be a legendary
silent film actor, or be an
anonymous but hugely influential
studio head?

◆

Would you rather work in
Bollywood or in Hollywood?

◆

Would you rather be a character in
a Manga cartoon or a character in
a Looney Tunes cartoon?

Would you rather have the job of replacing the cigarettes and guns in old movies with bananas and flowers, and some people hated you for it, or the job of directing movies that always, always had a happy ending and nobody ever did anything bad?

◆

Would you rather work with Andy Warhol or work with Steven Spielberg?

Would you rather live in the Marvel universe, or live in a terrible but ultimately harmless romantic comedy universe which probably features Hugh Grant, as usual?

◆

Would you rather have an elbow that randomly changed TV channels, or a television that would turn itself off if it didn't like what you were watching?

Would you rather be David Lynch
or be David Hasselhoff?

◆

Would you rather be the respected
personal trainer for an action film
star, and sometimes get smacked
in the face by accident, or be the
stuntman for an action film star
and know that you're probably
going to spend lots of your days on
fire, without getting their credit
and pay?

# TRIPLE TROUBLE/MORE
## FOUR KING QUESTIONS

Despite what politicians and ropey
referendums might have you believe,
not everything in life can, or should, be
reduced to a binary decision. With that
in mind, we've scanned the earth, air
and sea for some three and four option
concoctions. Although note that, way
back in the early 1970s, futurist Alvin
Toffler did wisely predict: 'People of the
future may suffer not from an absence
of choice but from a paralysing surfeit
of it. They may turn out to be victims of
that peculiarly super-industrial dilemma:
overchoice.' So, y'know, don't let these
additional options get you down, man.
It's only life, y'know?

Would you rather be Mozart, Elvis or Prince?

♦

Would you rather play bass like Lemmy, guitar like Phil Campbell, or drums like Mikkey Dee (you are obviously in the final lineup of the mighty Motörhead)?

♦

Would you rather be able to see a new colour, taste a new taste, or hear a new frequency?

Would you rather be an only child, one of a pair of twins, or one of a set of triplets?

◆

Would you rather be a big fish in a small pond, a small fish in a big pond, or be the person that is in charge of the pond?

◆

Would you rather be Captain Kirk, Captain Picard or Captain Janeway?

Would you rather be Bart, Maggie or Lisa Simpson?

◆

Would you rather lay an egg and have to keep it warm until it hatched, be pregnant for nine months and give birth to a helpless baby, or have a pouch that your offspring grows in until they're big enough to fend for themselves?

◆

Would you rather be a bird, a fish or a land mammal?

Would you rather have a McDonald's, a KFC or a Subway today?

◆

Would you rather take the Midnight Train to Georgia, a Mystery Train, or the Last Train to Trancentral?

◆

Would you rather have a secret admirer, be a secret admirer, or have a tempestuous relationship with someone you thought would be your perfect match?

Would you rather watch your best friend marry the person you are secretly in love with, or watch your best friend marry the person you secretly despise, or marry your best friend?

◆

Would you rather face a Zombie, a Draclea or a Frankensteins?

Would you rather drive your car
through a load of boxes whilst
being chased by baddies, or drive
your car through a fruit market
whilst being chased by the police,
or jump out of your car just before
it flies over a cliff and it explodes on
the rocks below so everyone thinks
you're dead, but DA DA DAAAAA
you live to fight another day?

♦

Would you rather only ever eat
breakfast, dinner, or tea?

Would you rather wake up from a nightmare, or wake up from a nightmare then realise you are still in the dream, or wake up from a nightmare then realise you are still in the dream and actually be in a movie?

◆

Would you rather have a cat that could tell you the weather forecast, a dog that could tell you the traffic conditions, or a goat that could do your homework (but homework that would stink of goat)?

Would you rather be able to pause, erase, or fast-forward significant moments in your life?

◆

Would you rather be a juggler, a gigolo, or a juggalo?

◆

Would you rather be a sock-cooker, a money-funster or a winker?

Would you rather have a ticket to ride, be a paperback writer, or be the walrus?

◆

Would you rather have three wishes (but one of them could not be 'infinite wishes'), have the power to change people's minds, or have the ability to make the best of every situation?

Would you rather get rid of summer, winter, spring or autumn? Would you rather live in the north, east, south or west?

◆

Would you rather be John, Paul (the real one), George or Ringo?

◆

Would you rather date Tinky-Winky, Dipsy, Laa-Laa or Po?

Would you rather shout 'Fore' like a golfer, make Petit-Fours like a top chef, know all the songs by the Four Tops, or be the fastest human on all fours?

◆

Would you rather fight Pestilence, Famine, Wild Beasts or Plague? (You can be on or off a horse; it's up to you.)

# FINALLY...

**WE HOPE YOU'VE** enjoyed chewing over some of the questions, dilemmas, conundrums and choices in this book. Whether they've been the start of a new conversational tangent, a bit of fun or a hard-fought games evening, there's much to be said for the art of talking to and connecting with each other. Maybe you've learnt something about each other and even, we might venture, yourself. Maybe you've not learnt a gosh-darned thing, and that's totally groovy too. This life would be dull without a modicum of chance added to it, wouldn't it? It's what keeps things interesting.

That all said, the Calvinist theory of predestination posits that we are all essentially subject to a universal determinism in that god is omniscient and therefore knows which way we will always turn. Because the deity is not bound by linear time in the same way that we are, the past, present and future are meaningless. To extrapolate: free will is a useful but ultimately flimsy illusion we buy into, to protect ourselves from the reality that eternity, being infinite, has always been there and always will be there. Indeed, the very concept of time as we understand it is utterly irrelevant. All decisions we think we make, in that context, are predestined. Human agency cannot be said to exist if temporality is observed as a concurrent whole by the omnipotent, for whom all decisions are thus always concurrently true, false and neutral.

Have a lovely evening, folks. Try the salmon. I'm here all week.

Joe

# ABOUT THE AUTHOR

**JOE SHOOMAN** has written words on music, entertainment, sport, news and crisps for many national newspapers and magazines over the years, and has worked in radio and occasionally on telly as a presenter, producer and reporter.

Joe is an intermittent contributor to the legendary *Viz* comic and is the author of numerous books on musicians, punk, Internet culture and more.

He once was sacked from his newspaper column for hiding rude messages about his team's rivals in the text. He lives on the smudgy borders between countries, realities, wakefulness and sleep, and contrary to popular rumours, does NOT like to move it, move it.

He is a registered Lord of Sealand, and as an Internet Reverend is also qualified to perform legal marriages in forty-eight US states.

Joe wrestles with innumerable questions constantly, and is still not sure whether he'd rather be an astronaut or a footballer when he grows up.

Or, indeed, whether he wants to ever grow up at all.

This book was also edited by James 'MC Ragamuffin' Hodgkinson. It's largely his fault in the first flipping place.

*Would You Rather...*
*Start a campaign for an inevitable*
*sequel?*

*Not flicks, but chill?*

*Buy other books by Joe Shooman?*

Contact us on Twitter: @jblakebooks
Or Tweet the author: @joeshooman

Huge thanks to Rachel Walsh
(www.rachelwalsh.co.uk
rachel.s.walsh@hotmail.com)
for the boss pics which are
totally ace.

# OTHER BOOKS BY JOE SHOOMAN:

*Bruce Dickinson: Maiden Voyage*
The definitive unofficial biography of the legendary
Iron Maiden singer, commercial pilot and renaissance
man. Foreword by Ian Gillan of Deep Purple.

*All Time Low: Don't Panic, Let's Party*
From Britain to Baltimore, these boys have taken pop-
punk to a higher level and continue to wow audiences
worldwide. But what really makes them tick?

*Blink* 182: *The Bands, The Breakdown and The Return*
An unparalleled look at the era-defining punks,
including exclusive and extensive interviews with
reclusive ex-drummer Scott Raynor.

*Kasabian: Sound, Movement and Empire*
The first ever biography of Leicester's finest – contains
a foreword by Engelbert Humperdinck himself.

*Trivium: The Mark of Perseverance*
So-Cal metalcore heroes' early days profiled,
including exclusive interviews with numerous ex-
members, engineers, family and friends.

ALL AVAILABLE IN PRINT AND EBOOK.